Dances

FOR TRUMPET AND PIANO   John McCabe

trumpet

CONTENTS

Total duration about 10 minutes

NOVELLO PUBLISHING LIMITED
8/9 Frith Street, London W1V 5TZ
Exclusive distributors:
Music Sales Limited
Newmarket Road, Bury St Edmunds, Suffolk IP33 3YB

Order No: NOV 120530

To Michael J. Easton

DANCES
for trumpet and piano
by
JOHN McCABE

TRUMPET IN B♭

1 POLISH DANCE

Allegro deciso ♩ = *c.* 120

2 BALLAD

Andantino soave ♩ = c.56

3 P. B. BLUES

4 HALLING

5 HIGHLAND HABANERA

6 SICILIANO

7 JIGAUDON

Dances

OR TRUMPET AND PIANO John McCabe

or trumpet and piano
RADES V AND VI

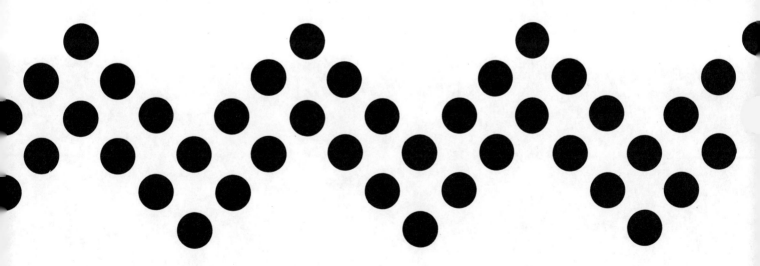

NOVELLO PUBLISHING LIMITED

8/9 Frith Street, London W1V 5TZ

rder No: NOV 120530

CONTENTS

Total duration about 10 minutes

Introduction

The gap between starting to learn an instrument and playing 'real' music is a very great deterrent to many players. Consequently, I, and some other composers got together to tackle this problem.

We are producing a series of pieces for many different instruments, playable by musicians with limited technical ability. As a guide, each has a grading similar to those of the Associated Board of the Royal Schools of Music, but I hope people of all grades will enjoy playing them.

Richard Rodney Bennett

Richard Rodney Bennett
Series Editor

To Michael J. Easton

DANCES
for trumpet and piano
by
JOHN McCABE

1 POLISH DANCE

1' 25"

2 BALLAD

1' 15"

3 P. B. BLUES

*Throughout this piece, change pedal at each change of chord.

8

4 HALLING

The quotation in the first two bars of this piece is from Grieg's *Slåtter*, Opus 72.

1' 35"

5 HIGHLAND HABANERA

1' 35"

6 SICILIANO

7 JIGAUDON

20

Printed in Great Britain by Headway Press Ltd

11/95 (22901)